GuestSpot

ANDREW LLOYD WEBBER
SHOWSTOPPERS
Playalong *for* Violin

Wise Publications
part of The Music Sales Group
London/New York/Paris/Sydney/Copenhagen/Berlin/Madrid/Tokyo

Published by
Wise Publications
8/9 Frith Street, London W1D 3JB, England.

Exclusive Distributors:
Music Sales Limited
Distribution Centre, Newmarket Road, Bury St. Edmunds,
Suffolk IP33 3YB England.
Music Sales Pty Limited
120 Rothschild Avenue, Rosebery, NSW 2018, Australia.

Order No. AM91953
ISBN 0-7119-4069-X
This book © Copyright 2005 by Wise Publications.

Compiled by Nick Crispin.
Edited by Christopher Hussey and Rebecca Taylor.
Music arranged by Quentin Thomas.
Music processed by Camden Music.
Cover photography by George Taylor.
Printed in Great Britain.

CD recorded, mixed and mastered by Jonas Persson and John Rose.
Violin played by Simon Baggs.
Backing tracks:
'As If We Never Said Goodbye', 'Love Changes Everything', 'The Phantom Of The Opera',
'Superstar' and 'Whistle Down The Wind' arranged by Danny G.
'Close Every Door' and 'Pie Jesu' arranged by John Maul.
'Don't Cry For Me Argentina' and 'Memory' arranged by Paul Honey.
'Unexpected Song' arranged by Jeff Leach.

As If We Never Said Goodbye

Music by Andrew Lloyd Webber
Words by Don Black & Christopher Hampton

Moderato

rit.

a tempo   piu mosso

molto allargando

a tempo

Close Every Door

Music by Andrew Lloyd Webber
Words by Tim Rice

Espressivo

a tempo

Love Changes Everything

Music by Andrew Lloyd Webber
Words by Don Black & Charles Hart

Dramatico ♩ = 92

Memory

Music by Andrew Lloyd Webber
Words by Trevor Nunn after T.S.Eliot

The Phantom Of The Opera

Music by Andrew Lloyd Webber
Words by Charles Hart

Allegro vivace

Fade to the end

Pie Jesu

Music by Andrew Lloyd Webber

Lento ♪ = 76 poco rall. a tempo

Don't Cry For Me Argentina

Music by Andrew Lloyd Webber
Words by Tim Rice

Slowly

Slow tango feel

poco rall.   **Slower**

Tempo 1º

Slower and freely

rit.　　　　　　　　　　　　**Refrain grandioso**

molto
allargando　　　　　a tempo

Superstar

Music by Andrew Lloyd Webber
Words by Tim Rice

Repeat 2 times and fade towards end

Unexpected Song

Music by Andrew Lloyd Webber
Words by Don Black

rall.   **Slower**

Whistle Down The Wind

Music by Andrew Lloyd Webber
Words by Jim Steinman

Moderato con moto

molto allargando   a tempo, broadly

rall.